NOVELLO CLOSE HARMONY POPULAR CLASSICS

ANYTHING GOES

& THREE OTHER SONGS

ARRANGED BY DAVID NIELD

BOOK ②

Novello

Music of the sort collected in this book is immediately likeable, and it seems to transcend fashion: there is rarely any objection that it is out of date or inaccessible. David Nield, a teacher and choir director of long experience and immense understanding (he taught me!) has achieved here the feat of choosing good music and making sure that his arrangement keeps the spirit of the original solo in choral form without making it difficult to sing.

One or two things will help make an effective performance. With young singers, a mature bass may be added to the bottom part, because that helps to keep everyone in tune. Or the bass may be doubled with an instrument. A light kit drum part will help keep the beat steady and add colour. There is no rule that close harmony always has to be unaccompanied, so other instruments may be added. This style of music is best presented without copies, if only because that is often the only way of making the singers look up at their audience. In any case, the rhythms of this style of music are often obscured by notation, and we can remember them more easily by ear. Choreography will often make a performance far more effective, and the singers themselves will usually be ready to offer their own suggestions for movement. If the singers are putting everything into the performance, the listeners are far more likely to enjoy themselves too.

RALPH ALLWOOD

Cover designed by Michael Bell Design.

NOV955064
ISBN 1-84609-164-0

© 2005 Novello & Company Limited.
Published in Great Britain by Novello Publishing Limited.

HEAD OFFICE
8/9 Frith Street, London W1D 3JB, England
Telephone: +44 (0)20 7434 0066
Fax: +44 (0)20 7287 6329

SALES & HIRE
Music Sales Limited
Newmarket Road, Bury St Edmunds, Suffolk IP33 3YB, England
Telephone: +44 (0)1284 702600
Fax: +44 (0)1284 768301

www.chesternovello.com
e-mail: music@musicsales.co.uk

Also in this series:
BOOK 1: SMOKE GETS IN YOUR EYES NOV955053
BOOK 3: A FINE ROMANCE NOV955075

Spread a little happiness

Words and Music:
Clifford Grey, Greatrex Newman and Vivien Ellis
arr. DAVID NIELD

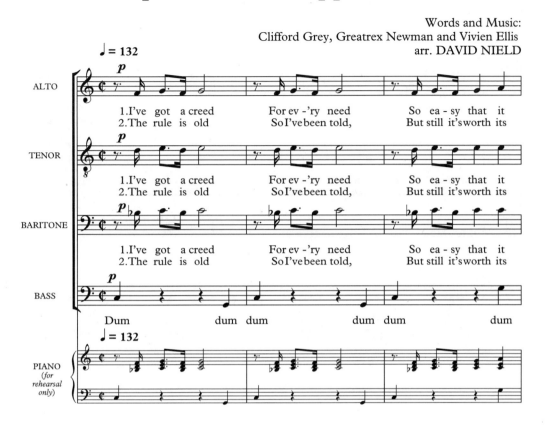

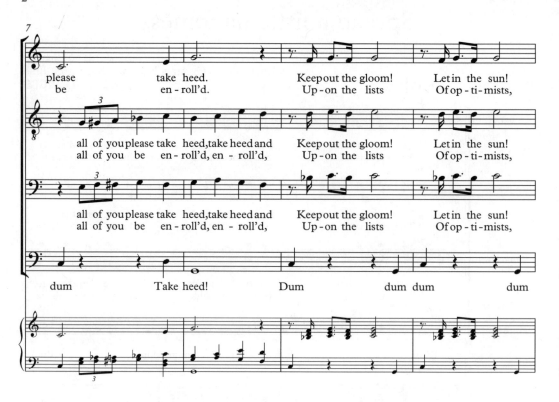

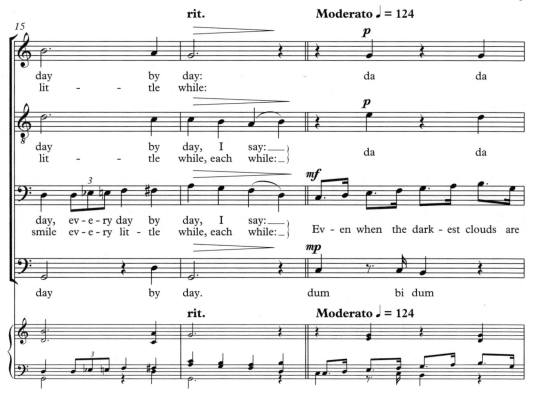

4

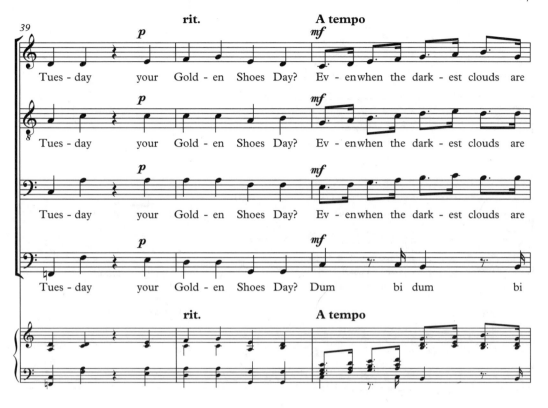

Singin' in the rain

Arthur Freed

Nacio Herb Brown
arr. DAVID NIELD

doo doo doo doo   doo doo doo doo doo   doo - di doo - di doo doo doo doo   doo doo

doo doo doo doo   doo doo doo doo doo   doo - di doo - di doo doo doo doo   doo doo

Sing - in' in the Rain.   What a glo - - ri-ous

doo   doo   doo   doo   doo   doo

da da da   doo doo doo doo   doo doo doo doo doo   doo doo doo

da da da   doo doo doo, doo   doo doo doo doo doo   doo doo doo

feel - ing, I'm hap - py a - gain,   I'm

da da da doo   doo   hap - py a - gain doo - di

*Optional cut to Bar 90

14

76

80

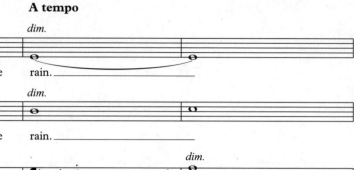

The Charleston

Jimmy Johnson

Cecil Mack
arr. DAVID NIELD

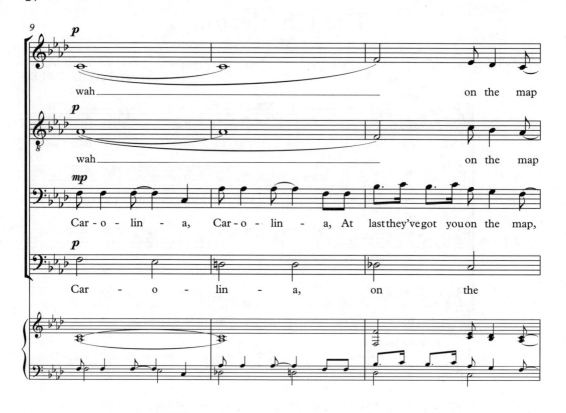

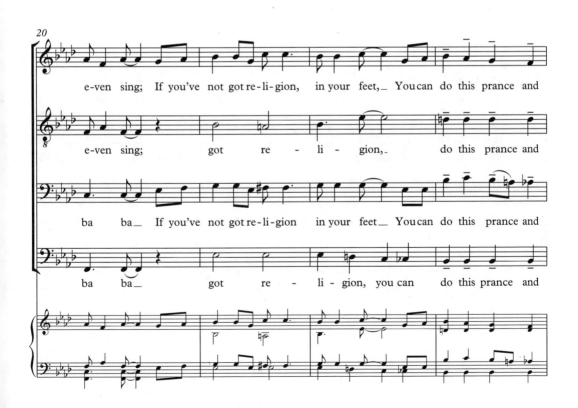

28

65

Charles - ton, _ ba da Charles - ton, _ ba da Gee, how _ you can

Charles - ton, _ ba da Charles - ton, _ ba da Gee, how _ you can

Charles - ton, _ ba da Charles - ton, _ ba da Gee, how _ you can

Charles - ton, _ ba da Charles - ton, _ ba da Gee, how _ you can

68

shuf - fle; _ Ev-'ry step _ you do, leads to some - thing new,

shuf - fle; _ Ev-'ry step _ you do, leads to some - thing new,

shuf - fle; _ ba da Ev-'ry step _ you do, leads to some - thing new,

shuf - fle; _ Ev - 'ry step _ you do, leads to some - thing new,

Charles - ton,_ the new Charles - ton,_ That dance_ is

Charles - ton,_ the new Charles - ton,_ I guess That dance____ is

Charles - ton,_ the new Charles - ton_ I guess That dance____ is

Charles - ton, the new Charles - ton, that dance is sure -

sure-ly a com - er, Some - time,_ You'll__ dance it

sure-ly a com - er, Some - time,_ I know You'll, You'll dance it

sure-ly a com - er, Some - time,_ I know You'll, You'll dance it

-ly a com - er, Some - time,_ I know You'll, You'll dance it

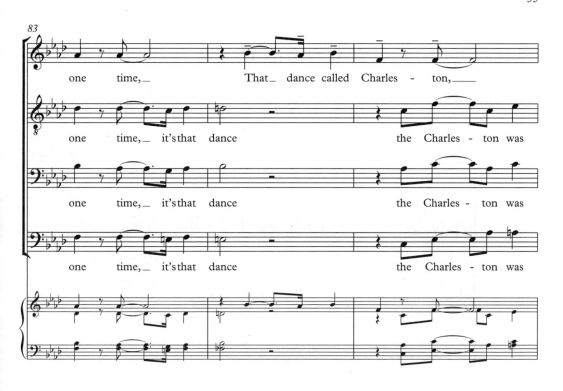

one time,__ That__ dance called Charles - ton,____
one time,__ it's that dance the Charles - ton was
one time,__ it's that dance the Charles - ton was
one time,__ it's that dance the Charles - ton was

molto rall.

made in South__ Car - o - line, made in South Car - o - line. Hoy!
made, made in South__ Car - o - line, made in South Car - o - line. Hoy!
made, made in South__ Car - o - line, made in South Car - o - line. Hoy!
made, made in South__ Car - o - line.____ Hoy!

molto rall.

Anything Goes

Words and Music: Cole Porter
arr. DAVID NIELD

8

Ply-mouth Rock. ___ If to - day, ___

Ply-mouth Rock. ___ If to - day, ___

Ply-mouth Rock. ___ If to - day, ___

Ply-mouth Rock, ___ oh, times have changed, ___ changed ___ Now we're talk-ing of to-

11

a - ny shock they should try to stem, ___ 'stead of land-ing on

a - ny shock they should try to stem, ___ 'stead of land-ing on

a - ny shock they should try to stem, ___ 'stead of land-ing on

-day A - ny shock they try to stem ___ in-

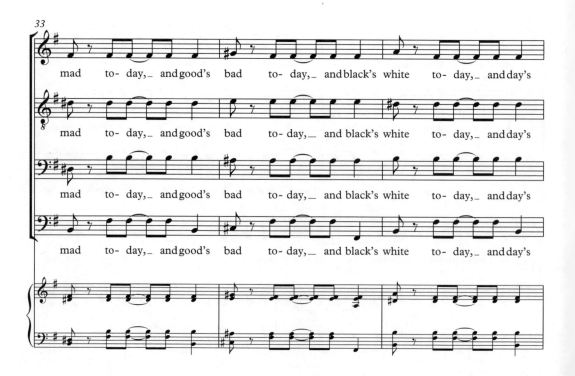

42

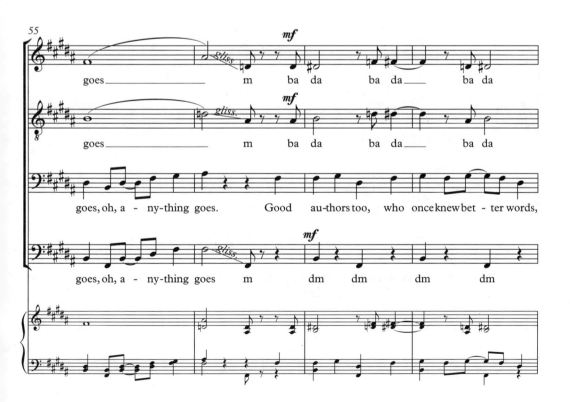

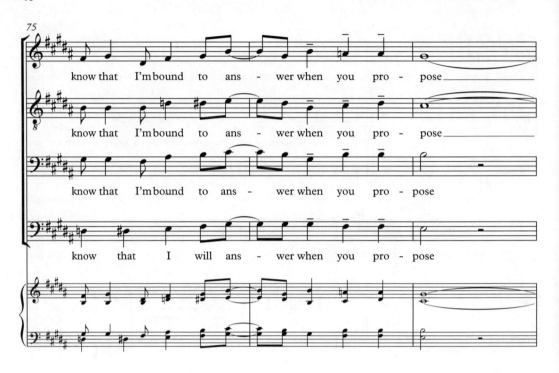